Confounding
CATCHPHRASES

Published and distributed by
TOBAR LIMITED
St. Margaret, Harleston, Norfolk, IP20 0TB, UK
www.tobar.co.uk

This edition printed 2005

Printed in Slovenia

ISBN 1-903230-21-7

02 Being in very good health

03 Unable to choose between two possibilities

04 Looking for an implied meaning in a text or situation

06 A misunderstood or embarrassing relative

08 Die: surrender a position of advantage

10 Awake and alert

12 Being grumpy and irritable

13 Of unsound mind

14 Leaving one's situation to chance

15 Attired in fancy or garish clothing

16 Being adamant

17 Where responsibility rests

19 Being put to a supreme test

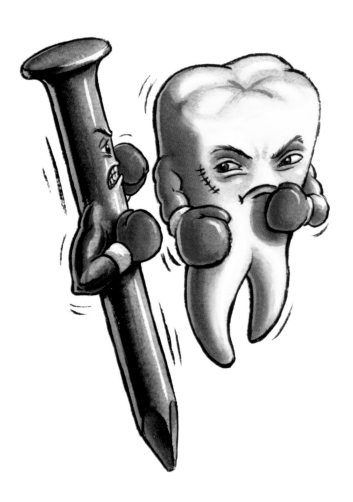

21 Battling fiercely

22 Exclamation of surprise

23 Delivering a statement or action with force

25 To keep a secret

27 Not making unnecessary fuss

28 Being hasty in embarking upon a course of action

29 Being near death

32 The wisdom of acting quickly

33 Concerning oneself in others' business

35 To inherit wealth upon birth

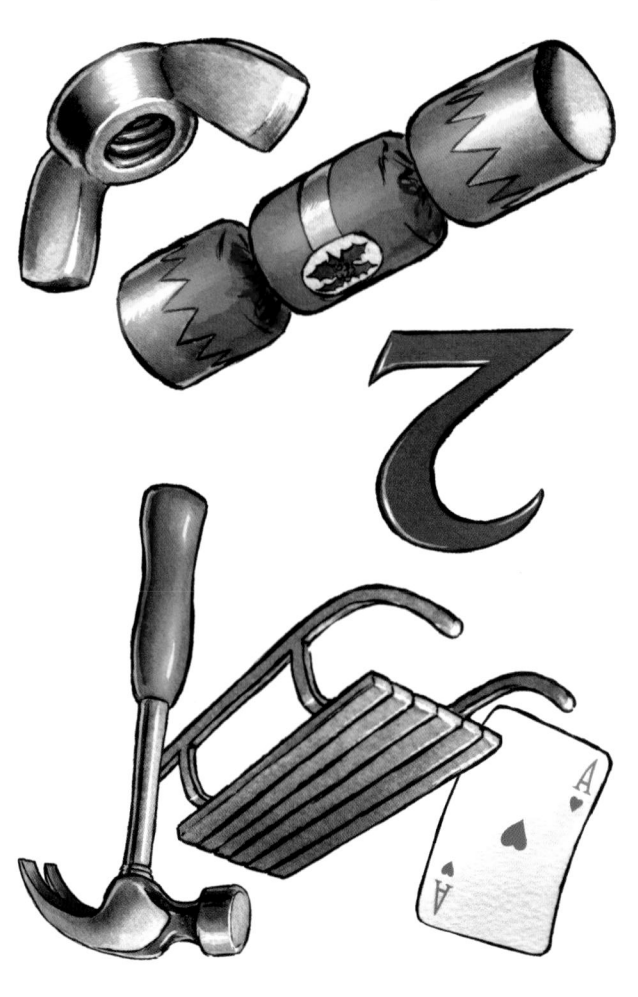

38 A description of events that is unbelievable

39 A single solution to multiple problems

40 Stirring up trouble

41 A situation more favourable than it at first seems

42 An evening of merrymaking

43 A heavy downpour.

44 The far-reaching powers of justice

47 Hoarseness; a temporary impairment of voice

48 Undoubtedly finished

49 Not adhering to regulations

50 Disclosing a secret

51 To spoil plans of arrangements

52 Someone who can turn his hand to many activities

53 Under maternal influence

54 An action that ensures failure

55 When blame falls upon two people

56 Affirmation of a statement's truth

57 An expression of rebuke

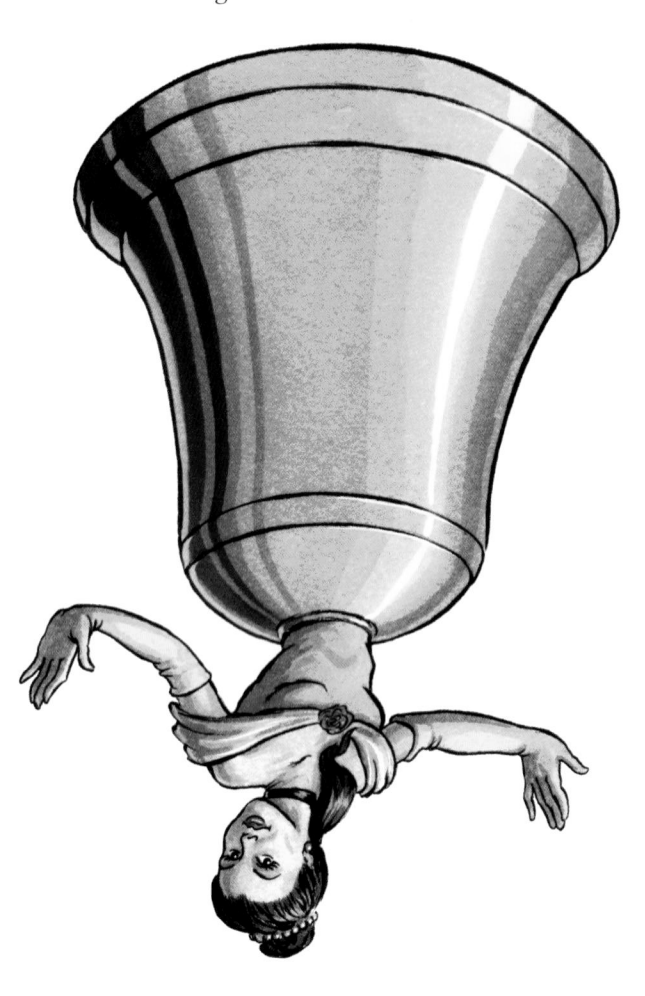

59 Straight-forward, without difficulty

60 A favourable position; a home in temperate climes

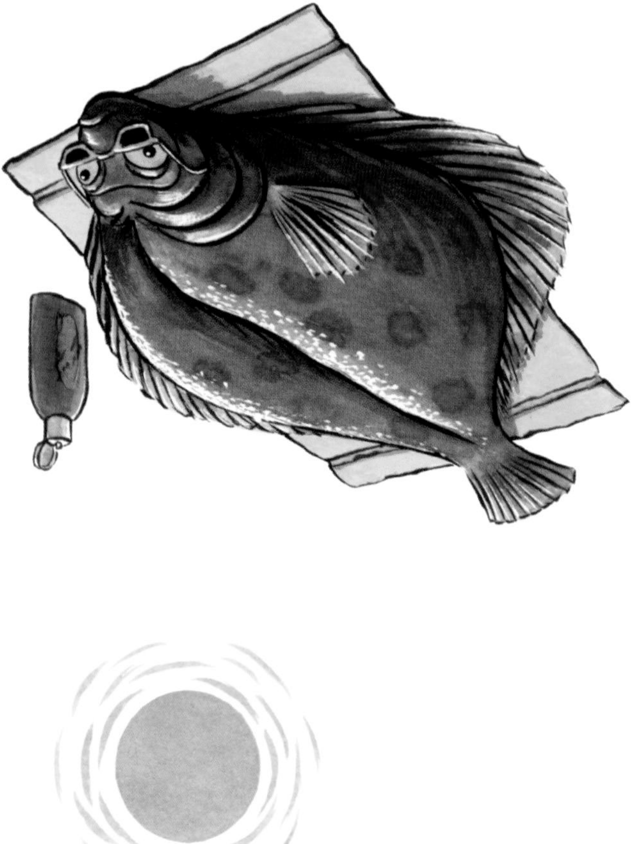

61 Disgraced or in disfavour

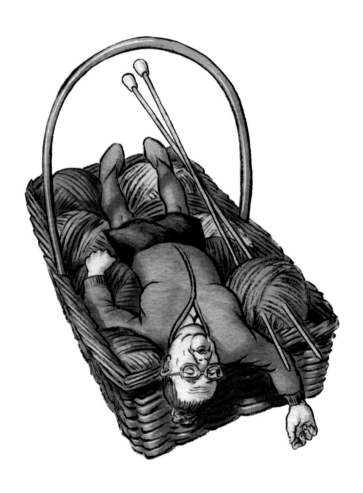

62 Unchanging in a belief or custom

63 Telling someone to leave

64 A clear and unchallenged victory

65 A complete change

66 An easy target

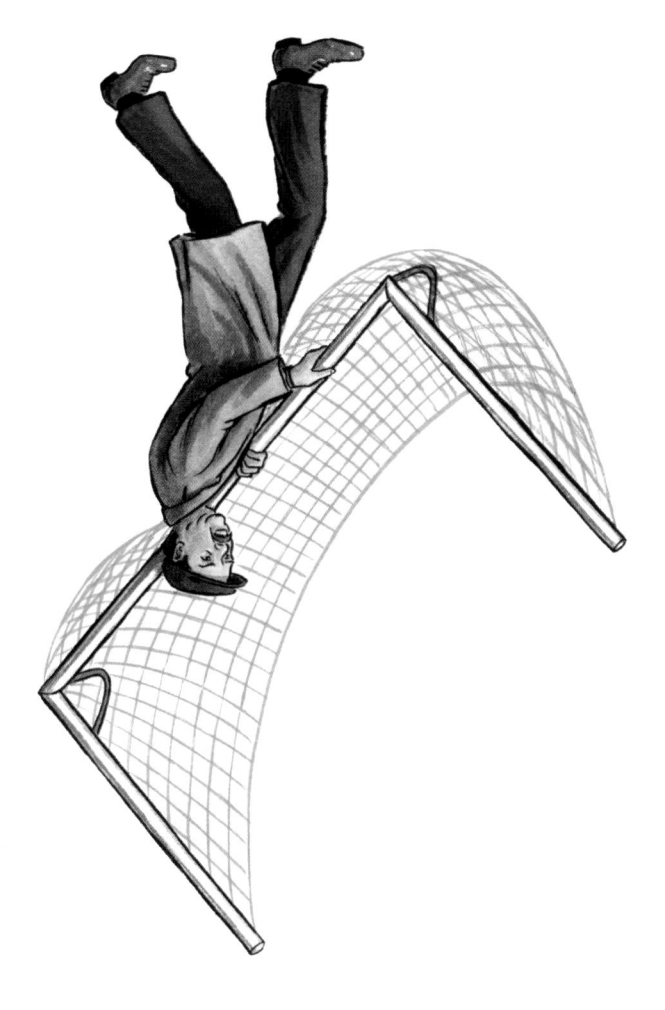

70 Losing one's temper.

71 To copy the actions of another

CATCHPHRASES ANSWERS

01 Dot the 'i's and cross the 't's
02 Fit as a fiddle
03 Fall between two stools
04 Reading between the lines
05 Running up a bill
06 The black sheep of the family
07 A diamond in the rough
08 Cash in your chips
09 Wolf in sheep's clothing
10 Bright-eyed and bushy tailed
11 Shooting the breeze
12 A bear with a sore head
13 Bats in the belfry
14 The luck of the draw
15 All dressed up like a Christmas tree
16 Digging in your heels
17 The buck stops here
18 An ugly duckling
19 Walking the plank
20 Catching the sun
21 Fighting tooth and nail
22 Holy Smoke!
23 Packing a punch
24 Hung, drawn and quartered
25 Keep it under your hat
26 Many hands make light work
27 Keep your hair on
28 Jumping the gun
29 One foot in the grave
30 Hold your head up
31 Getting on your high horse
32 A stitch in time saves nine
33 Poking your nose in
34 Dinner is served
35 Born with a silver spoon in your mouth
36 A sledgehammer to crack a nut
37 Lock, stock and barrel
38 A cock and bull story
39 Kill two birds with one stone
40 Rocking the boat
41 Blessing in disguise
42 A night on the tiles
43 Raining cats and dogs
44 The long arm of the law
45 An old head on young shoulders
46 A fish out of water
47 A frog in the throat
48 Dead as a dodo
49 Bending the rules
50 Letting the cat out of the bag
51 Upset the apple cart
52 Jack of all trades
53 Tied to mother's apron strings
54 The kiss of death
55 It takes two to tango
56 I kid you not
57 Put that in your pipe and smoke it
58 The belle of the ball
59 Plain sailing
60 A place in the sun
61 In the doghouse
62 Dyed in the wool
63 Sling your hook
64 Winning hands down
65 A clean sweep
66 A sitting duck
67 Moving the goalposts
68 Say it with flowers
69 Touching base
70 Blowing your top
71 Follow suit
72 Blowing a raspberry
73 Tilting at windmills